An ECS **Once Upon A Time**™ Book, Grades K-2

The Boy Who Cried Wolf

Critical Thinking and Writing Activities
For the Emerging Reader

Arlene Capriola and Rigmor Swensen
Illustrated by Kathy Burns

Welcome to the Once Upon A Time™ series!

Learning to read should be fun! Children focus longer and retain more when they are doing activities they enjoy. The 10-book **Once Upon A Time**™ series teaches reading and writing as a fun, engaging process. Children create their own storybooks (complete with illustrations!) by elaborating on well-known fairy tales. Familiar story lines and colorful characters will amuse and entertain children for hours as they improve reading and writing skills.

The **Once Upon A Time**™ series is more than just fun. It is an effective means of advancing reading and writing levels. Educators agree that emerging readers should begin reading with materials that provide higher-level thinking skills and practice in following directions. Research emphasizes that reading and writing should begin simultaneously. The **Once Upon A Time**™ series provides these elements in a format attractive to children. Each book in the series encourages:

- Reading beyond the blank before answering, learning to use context clues
- Rereading each completed chapter, asking, "Does your story make sense?"
- Referring to the story for clues to answer TELL and GUESS questions
- Becoming involved in the story and risk-taking
- Reading directions carefully prior to drawing comprehension pictures
- Using complete sentences for all writing activities

Welcome to the fairy-tale world of learning with the **Once Upon A Time**™ series! Have fun!

About the Authors...

Arlene Capriola, an elementary reading specialist, holds a combined master's degree in reading and learning disabilities. She has three sons and resides with her husband, John, in Long Island, New York.

Rigmor Swensen is a freelance writer and former teacher of secondary reading and English literature. She holds a master's degree in reading and special education. Riggie, mother of three, lives in Long Island, New York, with her husband, Roy. She and Arlene have enjoyed collaborating on several reading workbook series.

 The Once Upon A Time™ series is also available on audio tapes!

To order, contact your local school supply store or –

ECS Learning Systems, Inc.
P.O. Box 791437
San Antonio, Texas 78279-1437

Editor: Cherisse Mastry
Cover/Page Layout & Graphics: Kirstin Simpson
Book Design: Educational Media Services

ISBN 1-57022-143-X

My Story about...

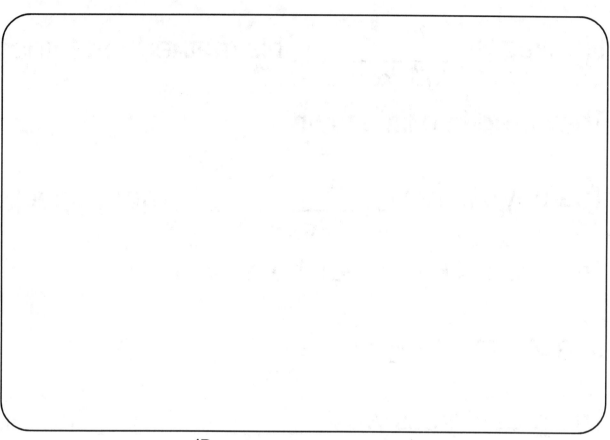

(Draw your own cover.)

The Boy Who Cried Wolf

by

_____

(Write your name.)

Chapter 1

Long ago there was a boy.

He lived _____ his mother and father.
(with, can)

They lived in a little town.

The boy's father _____ many sheep.
(was, had)

The sheep liked to eat the green grass.

It made them big and fat.

The green grass was _____ the hill.
(on, to)

Each day the sheep went up the hill.

_____ ate the good green grass.
(They, There)

They got _____ and fatter.
(bigger, top)

Tell: Who lived with the little boy?

He lived with _____

_____

Here are the sheep on the hill.

- **Draw** what they are eating.
- Make it the color in the story.

Chapter 2

One day the father called his _____ .
(son, apple)

"You are seven years old today," he said.

"It is time for _____ to help.
(big, you)

You must take the sheep up the hill to eat.

See that they get good _____ to eat.
(sand, grass)

See that _____ do not get lost.
(they, why)

And see that the wolf does not get them.

The wolf loves to eat the big, fat sheep.

If you see the wolf, you must call for help.

The others in town will _____ you.
(help, bring)

They will chase the wolf away."

Guess: What will the boy do the next day?

The boy will _____

_____

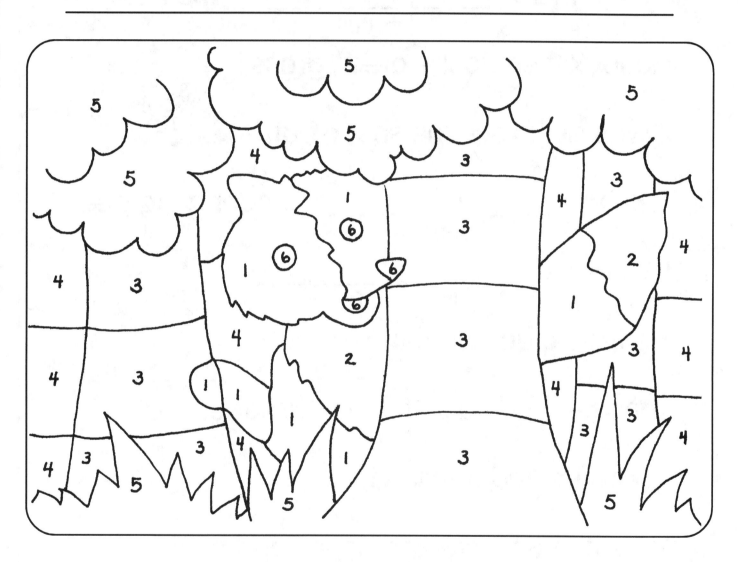

Who hides by the tree?

• **Color** the picture to see.

1 = red	3 = brown	5 = green
2 = gray	4 = blue	6 = black

Chapter 3

So that morning the boy took his sheep.

He led them _____ the hill.
(up, out)

He took them to the green grass.

It was fun to see the sheep eat.

The boy _____ under a big tree.
(sat, bit)

He sang a _____ .
(book, song)

He read a good book.

Then he made a picture in the sand.

At last he had nothing to _____ .
(go, do)

He sat and he sat and he sat and he sat.

He wanted _____ play.
(with, to)

But there was no one to play with.

Guess: How does the boy feel?

The boy _____

_____

Finish this picture of the boy on the hill.

- In box **2** put lots of grass.
- In box **3** put a book by the boy.
- In box **1** put a big sun up in the sky.

Chapter 4

The boy _____ down at the town.
(looked, made)

There on the hill was an old woman.

A little girl was with _____ .
(bat, her)

They had three big bags of flour.

"I wish they were here with me," said the boy.

So he called, "Wolf! Wolf! Help! Help!

The wolf _____ here.
(by, is)

He wants to eat the _____ .
(hats, sheep)

Please help me!"

The woman and the girl let the bags drop.

The flour fell _____ of the bags.
(out, next)

Tell: Is there a wolf by the sheep?

_____ , there _____
(Yes, No)

_____

The old woman and the girl run to help the boy.

• Help them get there fast.
• Go the A-B-C way.

Chapter 5

The woman and the girl ran to help the boy.

"Where is the wolf?" _____ called.
(we, they)

"We will beat him with our big stick!"

But _____ boy just smiled.
(so, the)

"There is no wolf," he said.

It is not fun on this _____ all day.
(hill, log)

I want you to play with me."

But the woman and the girl were mad.

"You did a very _____ thing," said the girl.
(top, bad)

"I lost all the flour," said the woman.

"Now we will have nothing to _____ !"
(eat, pay)

Guess: What will the boy's father say?

The boy's father will _____

_____

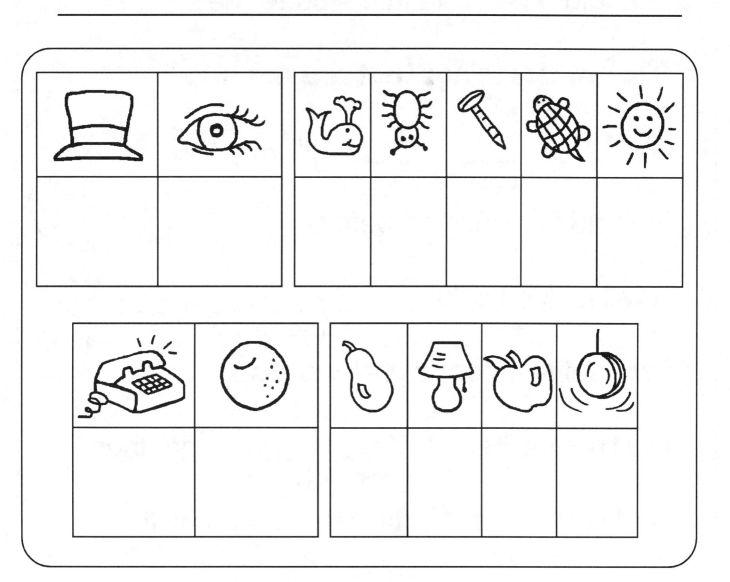

Why did the boy call, "Wolf! Wolf?"

• **Write** the first letter for each picture to see.

Chapter 6

That night the boy's _____ was mad.
(father, kitten)

"You did a very bad thing today," he said.

"Do not say things that are not true."

The _____ felt very sad.
(boy, ball)

He said he would be better.

"I will look after the _____ .
(tree, sheep)

I will get them good green grass.

I will not let the _____ get them.
(hen, wolf)

And I will not cry 'Wolf!' if there is no wolf."

That _____ the boy's father happy.
(sent, made)

Guess: Will the boy take the sheep again?

The boy _____

_____

Make the picture tell the story.

- Put **1** in the box that comes **first**.
- Put **2** in the box that comes **next**.
- Put **3** in the box that comes **last**.

Chapter 7

The next day the boy led his sheep up the hill.

He took them to the best _____ grass.
(green, red)

The boy _____ under the big tree.
(put, sat)

He sang a song to the wind.

He read a good _____ .
(book, lamp)

Then he took a nap.

After lunch the boy sat under the tree again.

He sat and he sat and he sat and he sat.

How he wanted _____ play!
(to, see)

But the sheep did _____ play.
(up, not)

Guess: What will the boy do now?

Now the boy will _____

_____

Make the Picture

- Show one thing the boy did in Chapter 7.

Chapter 8

The boy _____ very sad.
(felt, did)

He had been on the _____ all day.
(hop, hill)

How he wanted a friend!

Just then, he _____ a man and a boy.
(saw, hid)

They had big pails of water.

The boy called out, "Wolf! Wolf! Help! Help!"

The man and the boy let the pails drop.

All the _____ ran down the hill.
(water, wind)

They ran to the top of the hill.

"Where _____ the wolf?" they called.
(is, can)

"We will help.

We will chase him with our poles!"

Tell: Can the man get the water back?

_____ , the man _____
   (Yes, No)

_____

Color our pictures:

• The man and boy had water in me. **Color** me red.

• We like to eat grass. **Color** us white.

• I like to eat sheep. **Color** me gray.

• The women had flour in us. **Color** us brown.

Chapter 9

The boy just smiled.

"There is no wolf," he _____ .
(said, was)

"It is not fun on this hill all day.

I want you to _____ with me."
(play, stop)

But the man and the boy were mad.

"You did a _____ thing," said the boy.
(bad, blue)

"I lost all the water," said the man.

"Now we will have nothing to drink!"

They _____ back to town.
(led, went)

They _____ about the boy on the hill.
(told, saw)

"He says things that are not true," they said.

Tell: Did the others like what the boy did?

_____ , they _____
(Yes, No)

_____

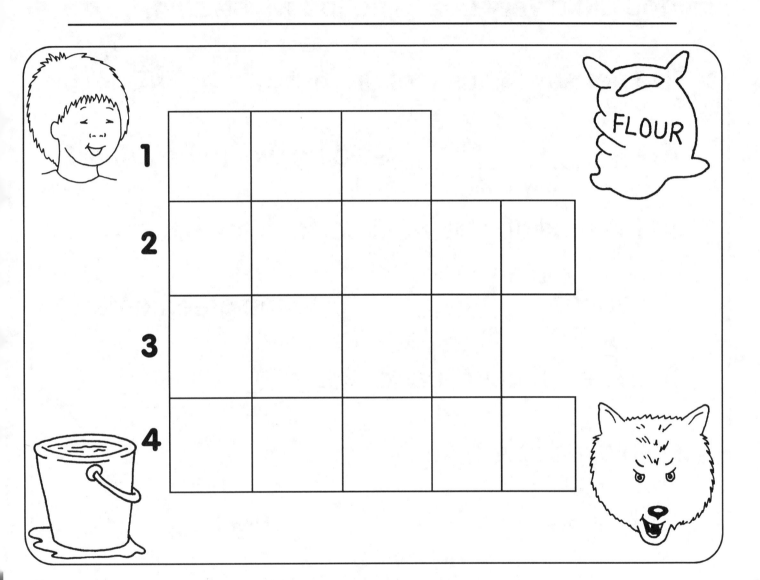

Write the word:

1. He wanted to play.

2. You can drink this.

3. The boy had to look for me!

4. This comes in bags.

Chapter 10

That night the boy's father was very mad.

"You did a **very** bad thing today," he said.

"Do not say things that are not true."

The _____ said he would be better.

(boy, bag)

So the next day he went back up the hill.

He led the _____ to the green grass.

(barn, sheep)

Then he sat down under the _____ .

(tree, train)

He played little games.

He looked _____ the wolf.

(of, for)

He _____ a song to the wind.

(sell, sang)

Just then, he saw something by the rock!

Guess: What is by the rock?

I think _____

_____

Here is the boy and his sheep.

- **Draw** the thing he is sitting under.
- **Draw** what the sheep are eating.
- Now **draw** the big rock he sees.

Chapter 11

A big gray wolf was looking at the sheep!

The boy called out, "Wolf! Wolf! Help! Help!"

"Ha, ha, ha," the people in town said.

"That boy _____ playing again."
(is, then)

Just then, the _____ jumped out.
(bug, wolf)

He grabbed a big, fat sheep.

"The wolf is here!" the _____ yelled.
(boy, wolf)

"He fooled us two times," the woman said.

"But he will not fool _____ again."
(she, us)

The boy yelled and yelled.

But no one _____ .
(came, find)

And the wolf ate all the sheep.

Tell: What will others do if you say things

that are not true? _____

_____

Here the boy calls for help.

• **Write** what he says.

• Now **write** what the people say.

Instant Recap

Here is the story of The Boy Who Cried Wolf again.
Write the words to tell the story.
The word box will help you.

Long ago there was a boy. He went up the hill with

his father's sheep. The _____ had to

see that the bad wolf did not _____ the sheep.

His father said, "If you see the wolf you must call for

_____ . The men and women in the

_____ will run up the hill. They will help

you chase the wolf."

The boy led the sheep up the _____ . He

took them to the grass. Then he had nothing to do. He

wanted to play. He wanted a _____ .

Just then, he saw a girl and a woman with bags of flour.

The boy called, "Wolf! Help!" They let the flour drop. It fell all over. Then they _____ to help the boy. They were very _____ when there was no wolf.

The boy's father said, "Do not say things that are not _____ ." The boy said he would be better.

The boy went back up the hill. Soon he wanted to _____ . He saw a man and a boy with pails of water. He called, "Wolf! Help!" They let the water drop. They were very mad when there was no wolf.

One day the wolf did come. The boy called, "Wolf!" No one came. The wolf ate all the sheep.

The End

boy	play	mad	true	friend
ran	hill	help	eat	town

Will you be my friend?

The boy says:

(This is the boy.)

I just wanted to play.
I just wanted a friend.
Will you be my friend now?

No ☐ Stop here.

Yes ☐ Go on.

(This is you.)

What is your name?

_____

Where do you live?

_____

How old are you? _____

Do you like to play? _____

Now I am happy!

In Jail?

Tell what the wolf did.

First, he hid _____

Next, he _____

This was _____ because _____
              (bad, not bad)

_____

We must ☐ put the wolf in jail.
        ☐ set the wolf free.

Did the wolf do a bad thing?
You be the judge.

Author's Page

You are the author.
Draw your picture in the box below.

1. **Read** your story to five others.

2. **Tell** them to put their names below.

3. Let them **tell** you how they like your story.

4. Let them **tell** you how they like your pictures.

_____
(Write your name.)